RAMAYANA STORIES

Prince Rama
in
Gurukul

An imprint of Om Books International

King Dasharatha of Ayodhya had four sons – Rama, Lakshmana, Bharata and Shatrughna. When they became adolescents, their sacred thread ceremony was held.

"This ceremony initiates you to life as students. Tomorrow, you will accompany

Guru Vashishtha to the gurukul to lead a life of simplicity and learning," King Dasharatha informed his sons after the ceremony was over. Guru Vashishtha was the royal priest and the Kulguru, or family teacher, of the Raghu dynasty.

All the boys were handsome and good-natured but Rama, the eldest, was especially loved in the royal household and throughout the kingdom. That evening, at dinner, Rama's mother Kausalya said to him sadly, "My son, this will be the last meal that we shall have together before you go."

"Why mother?" Rama asked.

"You will now go and live with your guru," Kausalya replied sadly. She was very fond of Rama and could not bear to be separated from him.

"Why can't you come with us, mother?" Rama asked innocently.

"The gurukul is the guru's family. From tomorrow, you are a part of the guru's family till your education is complete," Kausalya explained.

The next day, the four princes led by Rama accompanied Guru Vashishtha to the gurukul. Located on the banks of the holy river Saraswati, the gurukul had thousands of disciples. The plants and trees bore colourful flowers and fruits, and birds chirped, sang and flew about merrily.

Guru Vashishtha's wife Arundhati, the Gurumata, warmly welcomed Rama and his brothers. She looked after the gurukul and treated the students like her children.

"How does the gurukul provide so much food for everyone?" Rama asked a student one day.

"Lord Indra had gifted guruji a cow called Nandini. It is blessed with divine powers and gives us all the milk and ghee that we need. So we never have to worry about food."

In the gurukul, the four princes slept on the hard floor and ate simple food. They helped out with daily chores and mixed freely with all the disciples.

Guru Vashishtha was very happy with his new students, particularly with Rama. "All of them are gifted and clever, but Rama possesses a heart full of kindness and humility. He will be the perfect king for Ayodhya one day," Guru Vashishtha thought to himself.

Under his guidance, the four princes mastered all the aspects of knowledge, from the Vedas and Puranas to the arts and sciences. As Kshatriya princes, they also learnt military skills and the art of warfare. They learnt how to use a sword and fight with other weapons like the mace and the shield.

"A true warrior must be an excellent archer as archery is most important if you want to defeat an enemy in battle," Guru Vashishtha instructed the princes. Under his supervision, they learnt how to use the bow and arrow to perfection and practised shooting targets like an apple strung by a thread from a distant tree.

Although Lakshmana, Bharata and Shatrughna were excellent archers, by the time they finished their training, Rama was the best. The princes also became experts in chariot driving, horse riding and hunting.

One day, Guru Vashishtha informed the four princes, "Your time in the gurukul is over. I have taught you everything I know. You must return to Ayodhya. Now it is your duty to practise my teachings in your daily life. But always remember that whatever you have learnt here must be used to protect the weak and the helpless and never to hurt others."

"We shall never forget what you have taught us, Guruji." With folded hands, Rama spoke on behalf of all his brothers, "Please bless us so that we might succeed." The four princes touched their guru's feet.

"*Vijayi bhava* – be victorious always!" With that blessing, Guru Vashishtha bid the four princes goodbye.

Ramayana Stories

The Breaking of the Bow

An imprint of Om Books International

Demons had been disturbing the peace at Sage Vishwamitra's hermitage, so he requested Dasharatha, King of Ayodhya, to send his eldest son Rama to get rid of them. Rama and his younger brother Lakshmana killed the demons and restored peace in the hermitage. Sage Vishwamitra was pleased.

One day, he suggested to the brothers, "Let us leave for Janakpur."

"What is happening there?" Rama enquired.

"King Janaka has organised his daughter Sita's Swayamvara. She shall choose her husband through a contest. Great kings and nobles want to try their luck."

"What is the contest?" Lakshmana asked.

"Whoever breaks the mighty bow of Lord Shiva shall win Sita's hand in marriage," Sage Vishwamitra replied. "We shall be happy to accompany you," Rama said.

The three set off for Janakpur. On the way, Sage Vishwamitra explained, "The bow once belonged to Lord Shiva but is now in King Janaka's possession. Sita is King Janaka's adopted daughter. He had discovered her as a baby in a furrow while he was ploughing a field."

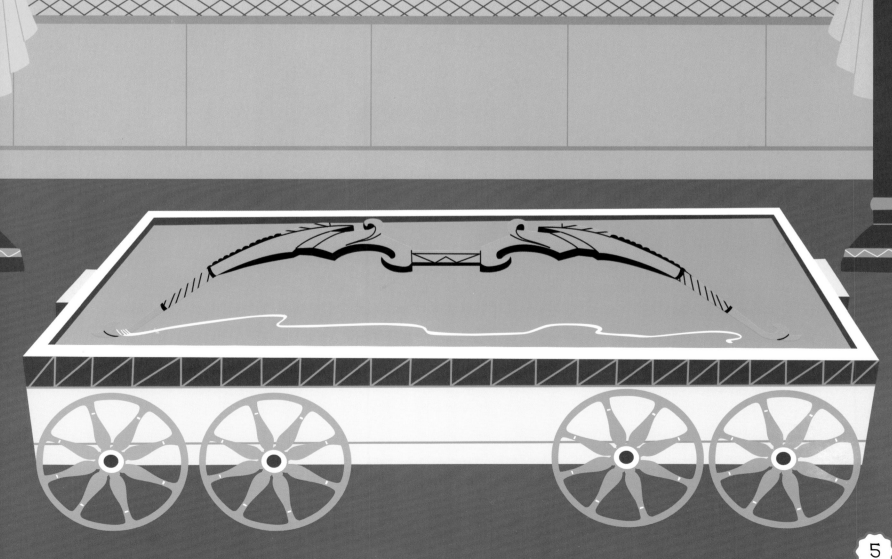

After a long journey, the three reached Janakpur.
A majestic city, it had lush orchards and gardens,
lovely lakes and ponds with fountains, and fine
squares and bustling markets. The royal palace had
bejewelled tapestry and staircases.

King Janaka received Sage Vishwamitra and the two princes warmly.

Impressed with Rama and Lakshmana's regal bearing, he asked Sage Vishwamitra, "O Sage, who are these warriors, resplendent like the sun and the moon?"

"The gems of the Raghu dynasty, the sons of Dasharatha, King of Ayodhya," Sage Vishwamitra replied. At dawn the following morning, Rama and Lakshmana visited the royal garden to collect flowers for their morning prayers.

There, Rama and Sita saw each other and were smitten. That night Rama slept late. He kept thinking about Sita. Early next morning, an excited Lakshmana woke him up, "Today is the day of the bow contest!"

"Yes, Lakshmana," Rama smiled.

9

Sage Vishwamitra, Rama and Lakshmana arrived at the palace, prepared for the contest. It was teeming with people.

"Have the bow brought in," King Janaka ordered. Five hundred men pulled in a large, eight-wheeled box with the bow.

"Behold!" King Janaka announced, "This is Lord Shiva's bow! When Sita was a child, she moved this bow. I had decided then that she would marry the man who could break this bow. Even mighty warriors like Ravana and Banasura could not do that."

Then Sita was summoned. As she entered with her companions, garland in hand, everyone was captivated by her beauty.

"Whoever can break this bow of Lord Shiva shall win the hand of the princess in marriage," the court bard announced. Many kings and nobles tried their hand but none could even lift the bow.

When everyone had failed, a saddened King Janaka said, "Alas! My daughter shall remain unwed as there is no hero amongst you who can even lift the bow, let alone string it or break it. Please return to your kingdoms as I cannot break my vow."

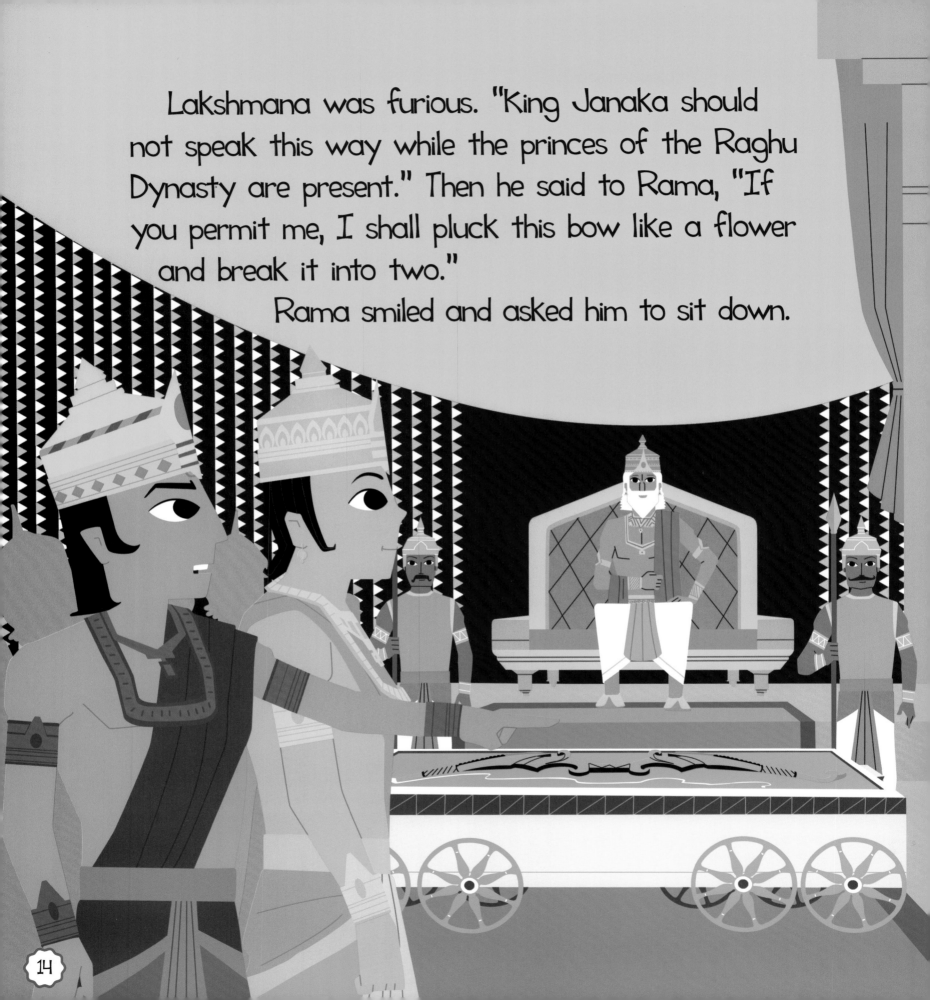

Lakshmana was furious. "King Janaka should not speak this way while the princes of the Raghu Dynasty are present." Then he said to Rama, "If you permit me, I shall pluck this bow like a flower and break it into two."

Rama smiled and asked him to sit down.

"Rama, go and break the bow," Sage Vishwamitra said. Rama bowed before Sage Vishwamitra and rose. He looked at Sita, who was seated on a throne, a vision of beauty and grace. Then he walked up to the box and lifted the bow with ease. The crowd was amazed. But as soon as he tried to string it, the bow broke into two halves.

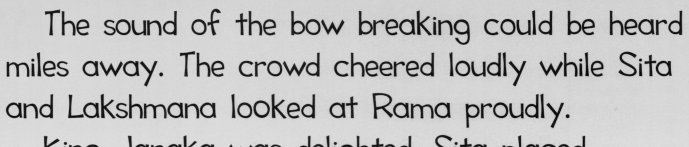

The sound of the bow breaking could be heard miles away. The crowd cheered loudly while Sita and Lakshmana looked at Rama proudly.

King Janaka was delighted. Sita placed the garland around Rama's neck and the two were united in holy matrimony.

RAMAYANA STORIES

The Kidnapping of Sita

Om KIDZ

An imprint of Om Books International

During their exile in the forest, Rama, Lakshmana and Sita arrived at Panchavati. "This place is so beautiful," Sita exclaimed.

"It is perfect to build our hut," Rama decided. So Lakshmana built a beautiful hut where they started living.

One day, the demoness Surpanakha saw them. Immediately, she was attracted to Rama. "How handsome is he! she exclaimed, "He will be the perfect husband for me!" Surpanakha transformed herself into a lovely maiden and approached Rama.

"Who are you, O ascetic, with bow and arrows?" she asked Rama.

Rama introduced himself, at which point
Surpanakha asked him to marry her.

"I am already married," Rama said, pointing
towards Sita.

"Marry me!" Surpanakha said to Lakshmana.

"I cannot marry a princess like you,"
Lakshmana replied.

"I'll kill your wife and eat her. Then you'll be free to marry me," Surpanakha said angrily to Rama and rushed towards Sita.

"Stop her, Lakshmana!" Rama screamed. In a flash, Lakshmana cut off Surpanakha's nose and ears with his sword.

"Oh, no!" Surpanakha cried before she assumed her true form and fled. Soon she returned with her brothers Dushana, Khara, and an army of fourteen thousand demons. Rama killed all the demons single-handedly while Lakshmana kept a watch over Sita.

Besides Surpanakha, only one demon called Akampana escaped by flying away over the southern ocean. Akampana landed in Lanka and met the demon king Ravana. "Rama, Prince of Ayodhya has killed your brothers Khara and Dushana," Akampana announced.

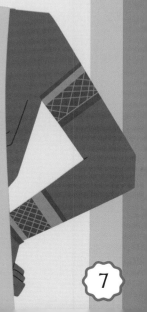

"How can my brave brothers be slain by a mere man?" Ravana said in disbelief.

Soon Surpanakha arrived. She wailed and told Ravana, "Look, how Rama and Lakshmana have treated me for no fault of mine. They have also killed our brothers. If you do not avenge this insult, no god or human shall fear us anymore."

Ravana immediately mounted his chariot and flew off to meet the demon Maricha. After informing Maricha about what had happened, he said, "I have a plan! Disguise yourself as a deer and distract Rama and Lakshmana so that I can kidnap Sita."

"Rama is no ordinary mortal," Maricha warned Ravana. "I was hit by his arrow at Sage Vishwamitra's hermitage and I was flung many miles away."

But Ravana was adamant. Maricha realised that he would be killed if he didn't follow his orders. Reluctantly, he went with Ravana to Panchavati. There, he transformed himself into a lovely golden deer.

The deer then pranced merrily towards the cottage where Rama, Sita and Lakshmana lived.

Spotting the animal in a bush, Sita exclaimed, "Look! What a beautiful deer. Please get it for me, my lord."

Rama followed the deer which led him far away from the hut.

After a long chase, Rama killed the elusive animal. But just as it fell to the ground, it cried out aloud, imitating Rama's voice, "Save me, Lakshmana!" Then the deer died, revealing Maricha's true form.

Sita heard the cry and told Lakshmana, "Your elder brother is in danger. Please rescue him."

"I'm sure Rama is all right," Lakshmana reassured her. But Sita insisted that Lakshmana went in search of Rama.

With his bow, Lakshmana drew a circle called Lakshmanrekha around the hut. "Please do not step out of this protective circle," Lakshmana said to Sita before leaving.

Immediately, Ravana approached the hut as a hermit. "Give me some alms," he begged Sita.

"My husband and brother-in-law are away, O sage," Sita replied. "Please wait for them to return."

"I am hungry. Please give me some food," Ravana pleaded.

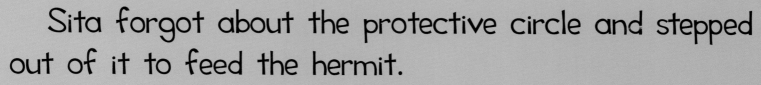

Sita forgot about the protective circle and stepped out of it to feed the hermit.

"I am Ravana, the King of Lanka," the hermit said. "Come away with me to be my queen."

Sita was furious, "How dare you? I am Rama's wife. You shall be killed for your impudence."

An angry Ravana dragged Sita out of the hut into his chariot. Then the chariot flew away towards Lanka.

RAMAYANA STORIES

Rama Meets the Monkey King Sugreeva

An imprint of Om Books International

Rama was heartbroken after Ravana kidnapped Sita. Along with Lakshmana, he searched the entire forest for Sita. Suddenly, they came across the vulture Jatayu, lying injured on the ground.

"O Rama! The wicked Ravana has kidnapped Sita," Jatayu said.

"I tried to stop him. But he chopped off my wings and claws after a fierce battle."
"O noble bird, where is Sita?"
Rama exclaimed.

3

"Ravana carried her off towards the south,"
Jatayu replied.

"Who is Ravana?" Rama asked.

"He is the king of the demons...and..." Jatayu tried
to speak before he breathed his last.

Sadly, Rama and Lakshmana cremated Jatayu and resumed their search for Sita. But when they entered the Krauncha Forest, a gigantic demon held them in his hands.

Just as he was about to swallow Rama and Lakshmana, they chopped off his hands with their swords and escaped.

"Stop!" the injured demon pleaded. "I shall help you! Burn me at once!"

Rama and Lakshmana burnt the demon and a handsome youth arose from the flames.

"O Rama! My name is Kabandha and I am a gandharva. Thanks to you and Lakshmana, I have been released from my curse. I shall help you. Go to Rishyamuka Mountains and meet the Monkey King, Sugreeva. He can help you find Sita," he said and disappeared.

Rama and Lakshmana crossed Lake Pampa to reach the foot of Rishyamuka Mountains. But someone was watching them.

"Who are those two men?" Sugreeva, the Monkey King exclaimed. "Are they spies or assassins sent by my evil brother, Vali? Send for Hanuman immediately," he ordered. Hanuman arrived and observed Rama and Lakshmana approach.

"It is rare for humans to enter our kingdom," Hanuman said. "They also look strong and purposeful. Let me find out who they are and what they want."

"But be discreet. Go in disguise so they are not suspicious," Sugreeva replied. Hanuman transformed himself into a brahmana and ran down the hill.

"Who are you dear sirs?" he asked Rama and Lakshmana. "Why are you wandering here? Are you ascetics, kshatriyas or gods?"

"We are Rama and Lakshmana, sons of King Dasharatha," Rama replied. "An evil demon called Ravana has kidnapped my wife Sita," Rama replied. "We are looking for her. But who are you, O brahmana?"

Hanuman immediately fell at Rama's feet.

"Pardon me Lord Rama. I could not recognise you," Hanuman said, revealing his true form. "I am Hanuman, son of Vayu."

Rama embraced Hanuman.

"We are looking for Sugreeva, the king of your monkey clan," Lakshmana said.

"It will be wise on your part to make Sugreeva an ally. He has an army of millions of monkeys who can search for Sita," Hanuman replied.

"Lead us to Sugreeva then," Rama requested.

"Why should you trouble yourself by trekking up the mountain?" Hanuman smiled and assumed a gigantic form. Then he bent down and said, "Please be seated on my shoulders and allow me to transport you to Sugreeva."

As soon as the brothers were seated, Hanuman leapt skywards and was in front of Sugreeva in a flash.

"I am fortunate that you have chosen to visit me," Sugreeva said warmly after Hanuman introduced Rama and Lakshmana.

"We are happy to finally meet you," Rama replied as the two embraced each other.

"Rama and Lakshmana are looking for Sita who has been kidnapped by Ravana," Hanuman

explained to Sugreeva and then said to Rama, "Our king needs a strong ally to defeat his brother and enemy Vali."

Rama and Sugreeva sealed their friendship with fire as their witness and pledged to help each other.

RAMAYANA STORIES

The Burning of Lanka

An imprint of Om Books International

Sugreeva, the Monkey King, sent his army in all directions to help Rama find Sita who had been kidnapped by Ravana. Before Hanuman set out, Rama spoke to him, "If there is anyone who can find Sita, it is you, O Hanuman! Take my ring." Rama removed a ring from his finger and handed it to Hanuman. "This ring will prove to Sita that you are my messenger." Hanuman journeyed southwards with his army of monkeys, escorted by bravehearts like Angada, the son of Vali and the crown prince of Kishkindha, and the old and wise bear Jambavana. Despite a long search, they were unable to find Sita.

"What are you looking for?" a voice asked from above. The monkeys looked up to see the vulture Sampati, the brother of Jatayu.

"We are looking for Lord Rama's wife Sita," Hanuman replied.

"I saw Ravana carry her across the ocean to Lanka," Sampati informed them.

Hanuman and the army of monkeys reached the ocean.

"One of us must go to Lanka to fetch news of Sita," Jambavana declared. "But who among us can cover such a vast distance to Lanka across the ocean? I could have done it in my youth but I am too old now."

"I can easily make the required leap," Angada stated. "But I'm not sure if I would

have the energy to return."
Then, turning to Hanuman, Jambavana said, "Only you can perform this task, O Hanuman."

Hanuman grew in size and soon he was as tall as a mountain.

Then, he leapt skywards and flew at breakneck speed before Mount Mainak arose from the ocean to stop him.

"Take that!" Hanuman struck the mountain a mighty blow.

"I am a friend of your father's," Mainak said to Hanuman. "Why don't you rest here for a while? You have a long journey ahead."

"I cannot rest until I have succeeded in my mission," Hanuman replied and continued his journey. After a while, he found his path blocked by the gigantic Surasa, the mother of serpents.

"You cannot pass without entering my mouth," she hissed. Hanuman grew in size and Surasa's jaws widened to accommodate him. Suddenly, Hanuman shrunk to the size of a fly, entered her mouth and escaped in a flash. Further, in his quest for Sita, Hanuman confronted Rakshasi Simhika who used her magical powers and swallowed him. But Hanuman grew in size inside her stomach and killed her by tearing through her body.

Finally, Hanuman reached Lanka at dusk and tried to enter the city unnoticed.

"How can you be so foolish to enter the city when I am guarding it?" The guardian deity of Lanka blocked Hanuman's path. But one blow from Hanuman sent her sprawling to the ground. As Hanuman entered Lanka, the guardian deity recalled, "According to a prophecy, the

rakshasas shall be defeated in battle if I am overpowered by a monkey. That day has arrived."

Soon, Hanuman entered Ravana's palace. "Let me now gauge the strength of the enemy before I return." He uprooted the trees of the grove as he went in search of Sita killing any rakshasas on the way. Then, he climbed the tallest tree to continue his search.

It was almost daybreak when Hanuman found Sita in the grove. He dropped the ring into her lap.

"Who are you?" Sita asked Hanuman who revealed everything to her.

"Let my husband come, destroy Ravana and take me back. Only then shall my honour be restored," Sita replied. "Take this jewel back to my lord," she requested Hanuman. Hanuman bade goodbye to Sita.

Hanuman destroyed the rakshasas who tried to stop him while on his way back. At last, Hanuman was captured by Ravana's son Indrajit.

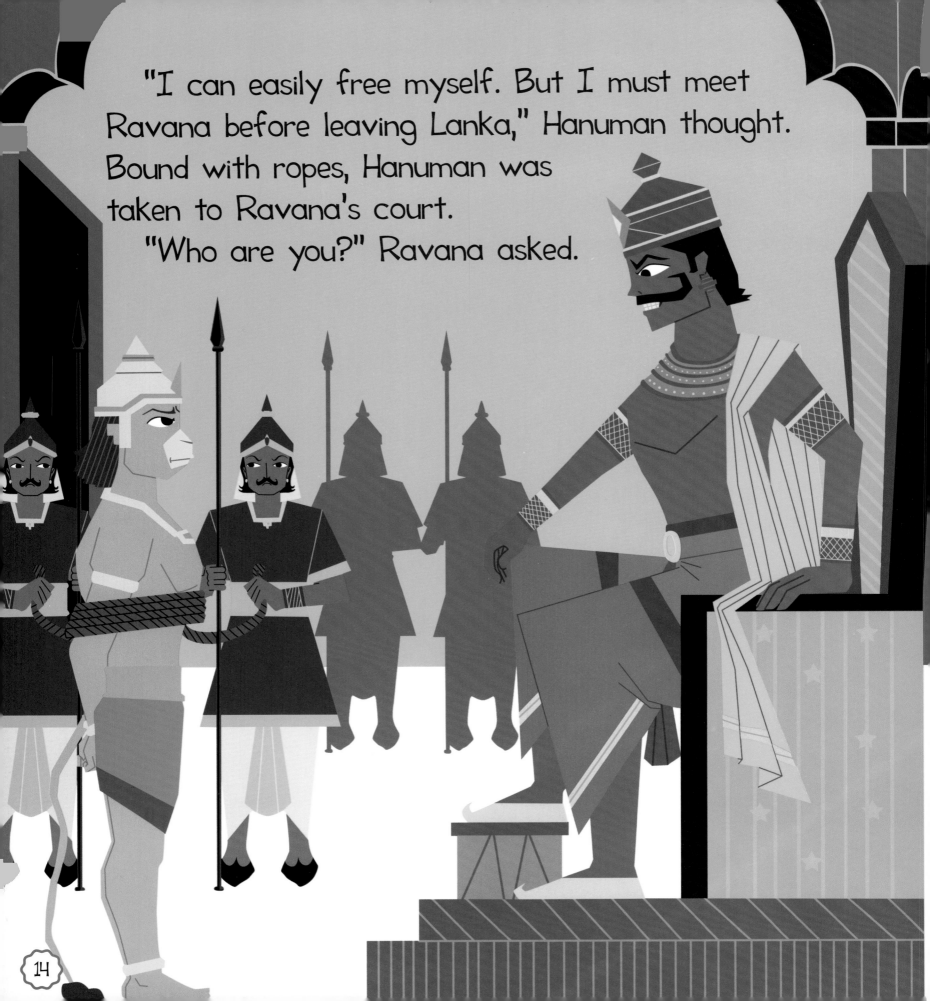

"I can easily free myself. But I must meet Ravana before leaving Lanka," Hanuman thought. Bound with ropes, Hanuman was taken to Ravana's court.

"Who are you?" Ravana asked.

"I am Hanuman, a messenger of King Sugreeva and Lord Rama. Return Mother Sita to Lord Rama or prepare to die."

"Kill this monkey!" Ravana ordered angrily.

"An envoy cannot be put to death!" Ravana's brother Vibhishana interrupted.

"Then set his tail on fire and parade him through the city," Ravana laughed. The rakshasas tied Hanuman's tail with pieces of cloth soaked in oil, and set it on fire. Then he was paraded on the streets of Lanka and all the rakshasas had a hearty laugh. But their laughter vanished when Hanuman assumed a gigantic form. He broke free from the ropes and jumped from one roof to the other, setting fire to the entire city of Lanka with his burning tail. Then Hanuman flew back to the other side of the ocean to join his companions.

RAMAYANA STORIES

The Building of Rama Setu

An imprint of Om Books International

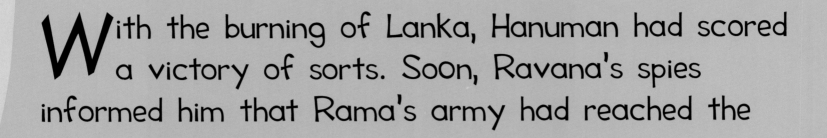

With the burning of Lanka, Hanuman had scored
a victory of sorts. Soon, Ravana's spies
informed him that Rama's army had reached the

oceanfront. Worried and troubled, Ravana summoned his ministers, who said, "We must kill those men and monkeys at once!"

3

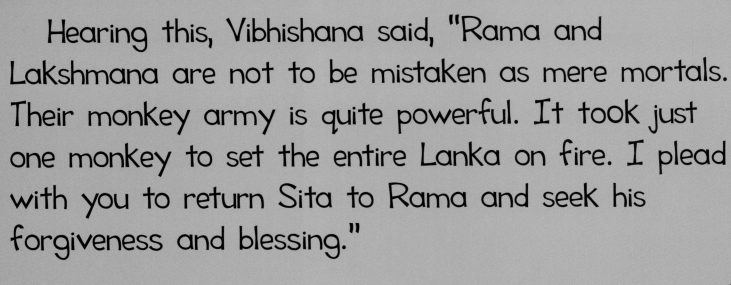

Hearing this, Vibhishana said, "Rama and Lakshmana are not to be mistaken as mere mortals. Their monkey army is quite powerful. It took just one monkey to set the entire Lanka on fire. I plead with you to return Sita to Rama and seek his forgiveness and blessing."

On hearing this, Ravana flew into a rage. He banished Vibhishana from his court saying, "If that's what you believe, go to Rama for support."

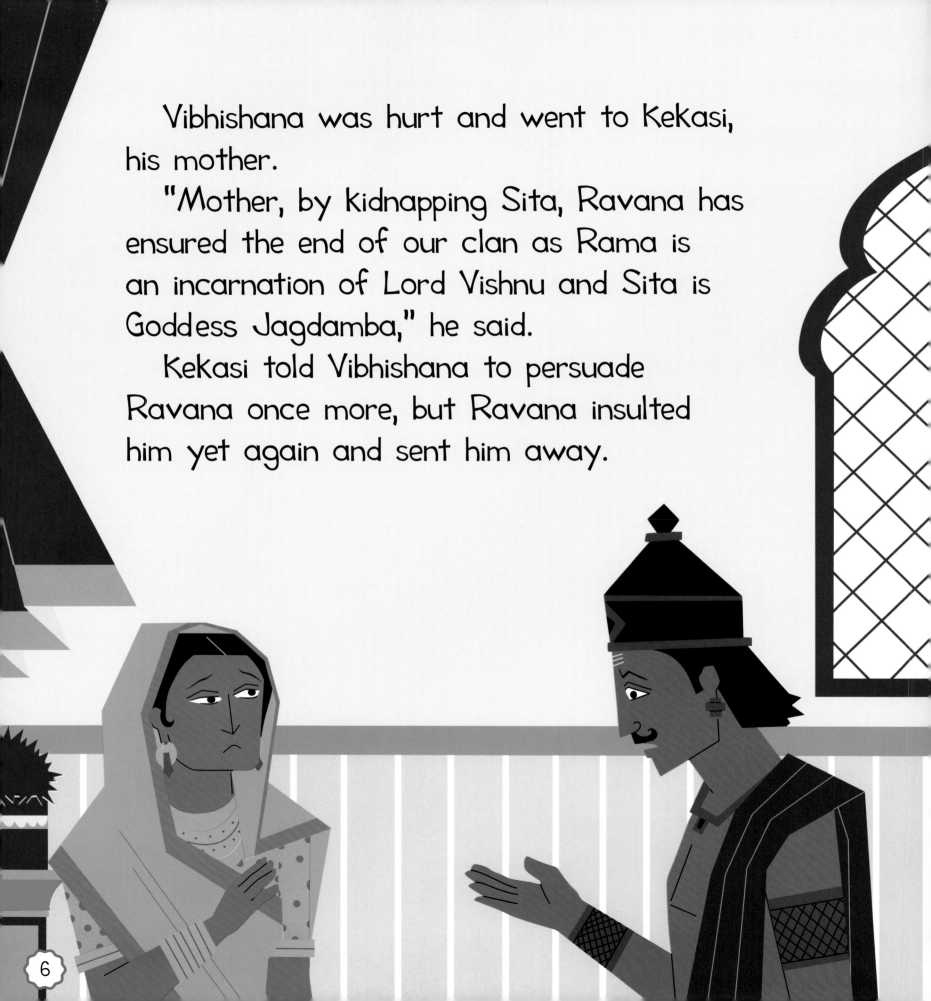

Vibhishana was hurt and went to Kekasi, his mother.

"Mother, by kidnapping Sita, Ravana has ensured the end of our clan as Rama is an incarnation of Lord Vishnu and Sita is Goddess Jagdamba," he said.

Kekasi told Vibhishana to persuade Ravana once more, but Ravana insulted him yet again and sent him away.

Vibhishana went to Rama. Some of the monkey chiefs viewed him with suspicion. But Rama said, "I will always accept whoever seeks my support."

Affectionately, Rama offered Vibhishana a seat by his side. He put a Rajtilak on his forehead and said, "You are the future king of Lanka."

The monkey chiefs made plans to cross the ocean. Everyone had a different suggestion.

Rama said, "I want to pray to the Lord of the Ocean to give us safe passage."

He sat in meditation, facing the ocean and began to pray. Despite praying for three days, he did not get any response. This made Rama angry. He then asked Lakshmana to fetch a bow and an arrow so that he could destroy the ocean and all within it.

Perturbed by Rama's anger, the Lord of the Ocean appeared before him. He begged to be forgiven for not heeding Rama's prayers. He suggested that they build a bridge to cross the ocean and offered all his help.

Rama prayed to Shiva for advice. Shiva too suggested Rama build a bridge, adding, "Nala and Nila, the two avatars of Vishwakarma, will help you in this task with their expertise."

On receiving orders from Rama, Nala and Nila began building the Rama Setu with the help of the army of monkeys. The monkeys brought huge stones and

rocks. After writing "Rama" on each of them, they tossed them into the ocean. With Rama's name on each of them, instead of sinking, the rocks remained afloat.

In their childhood, Nala and Nila, disturbed the rishis by throwing their vessels into the sea. One day, the rishis cursed them, "From now on, whatever you throw into water will not sink." This was another reason the rocks remained afloat.

After a few days of hard labour and dedication, the Rama Setu was ready.

Lord Rama ordered his army to advance to Lanka. In a short while, the army of monkeys crossed the newly built Rama Setu and reached the shores of Lanka. On reaching Lanka, Rama set up camp on the Suvela Hill. Rama and his army of monkeys would soon be on their way to Ashok Vatika where Sita had been kept imprisoned by Ravana.

RAMAYANA STORIES

The Battle Begins

Om
KIDZ

An imprint of Om Books International

Ravana's wife, Mandodari, learned about Rama's arrival at Lanka. Disturbed by the turn of events, she went to Ravana and tried convincing him, "Please send Sita back to Rama and seek forgiveness."

Ravana exclaimed, "You are not aware of my strength and might, Mandodari. Don't you remember how I lifted the

mighty Kailash Mountain? All gods are at my mercy. Rama is just an ordinary man and monkeys are our food. You want me to be fearful of them? Never!"

Mandodari stood by silently.

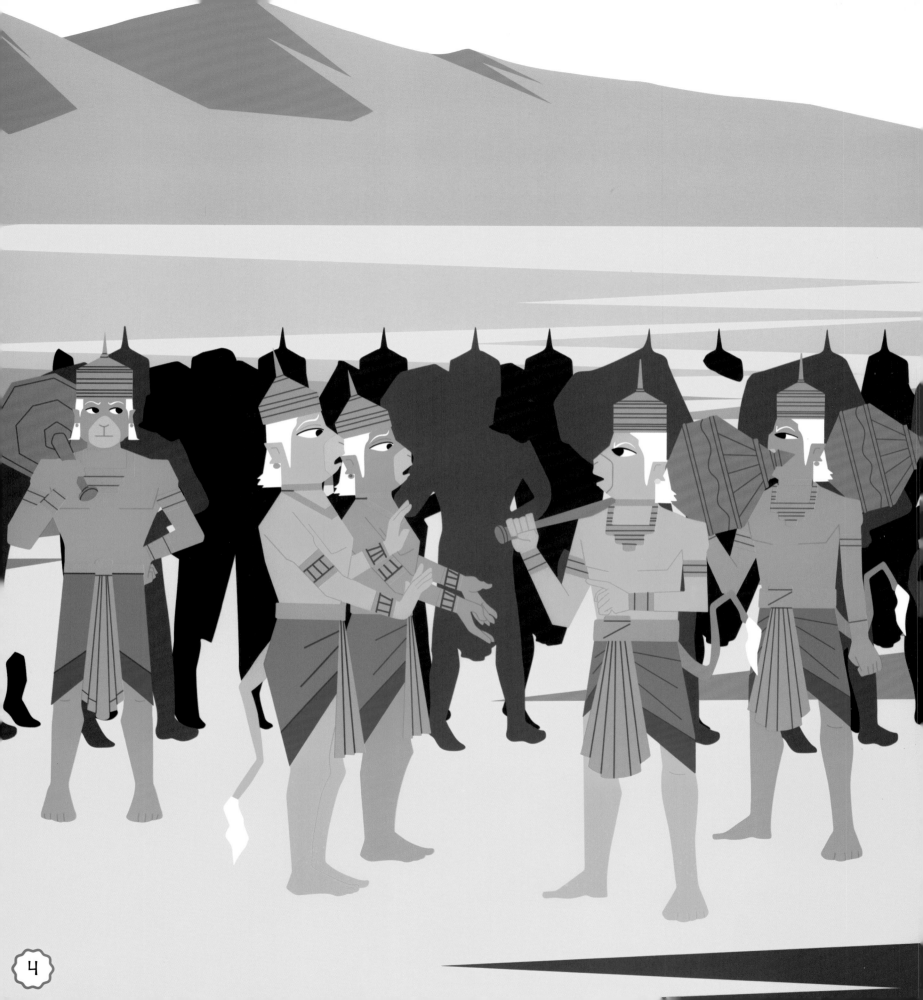

To assess the strength of his rival's army, Ravana sent two spies, Shuk and Saran, to Rama's camp.

Disguised as monkeys, Shuk and Saran slipped into Rama's camp. However, Vibhishana recognised Ravana's spies at once. The army of monkeys captured the spies and took them to Rama. Frightened, the spies sought forgiveness and pleaded for mercy.

Rama agreed to let them go, but before doing so, he announced, "Tell Ravana to return Sita or he will have to face dire consequences."

When Shuk and Saran told Ravana about Rama, he said furiously, "I will never return Sita to Rama. I am ready for battle."

Meanwhile, Ravana and Rama began preparing their respective armies for battle. After consulting his ministers, Rama sent Angada as an envoy to Ravana's court. He wanted to give Ravana a last warning.

When the Lankans saw Angada, they froze with fear. Whispering to each other, they said, "The monkey who destroyed Lanka has come back. What would he do now?"

Scared, all of them dispersed to make way for him.

When Angada reached Ravana's court, he introduced himself as the son of Vali and Rama's envoy. As instructed by Rama, he asked Ravana to return Sita and surrender. Ravana roared with laughter, "I will pardon your rude behaviour because you are my friend Vali's son. But I am amazed at your willingness to befriend the one who killed your father Vali!"

Ravana and Angada got into an argument. When Ravana refused to make peace with Rama, Angada stepped forward and said, "Before you begin the fight, try to move my foot. If you can move it even an inch, I promise I will lay down my arms."

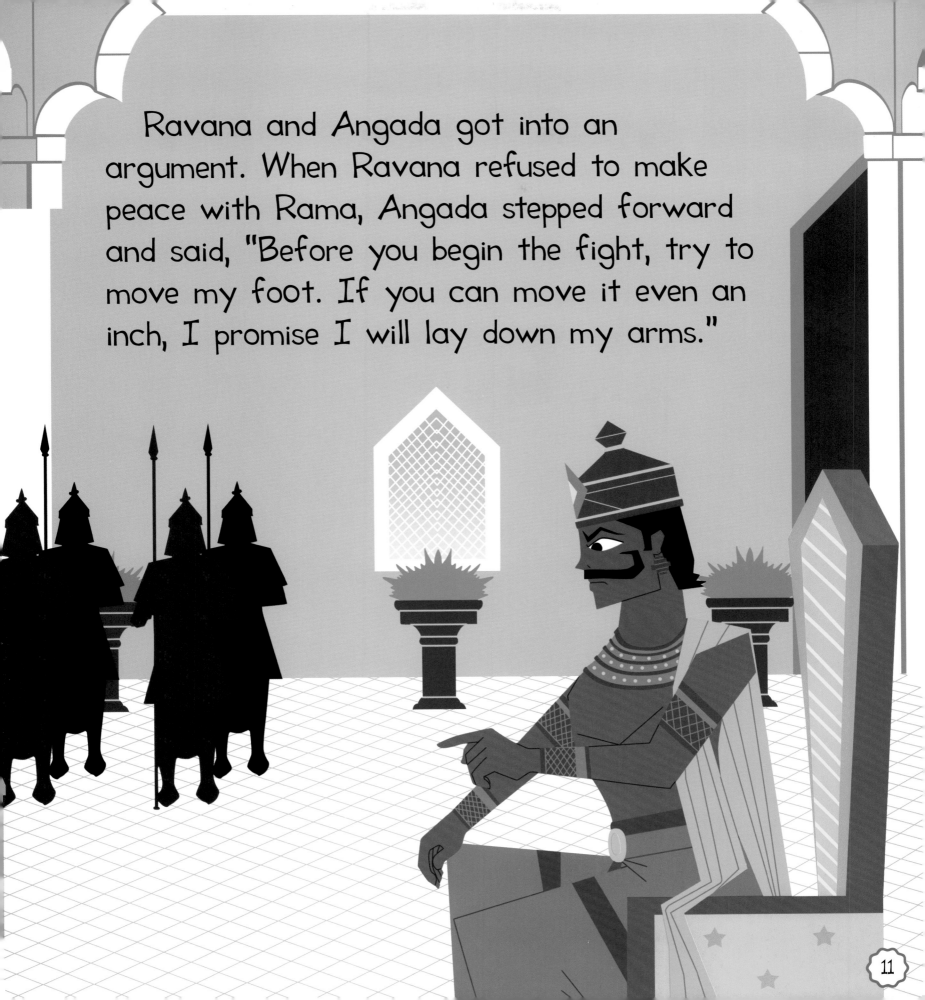

Ravana commanded his courtiers to hold Angada by his foot and throw him out. None of Ravana's courtiers could make him move. Finally, Ravana came forward. When he bent, his crown fell off. Angada picked it up and flung it away. Embarrassed, Ravana returned to his throne. Angada challenged Ravana again and returned to the camp after conveying Rama's message.

Ravana's mother Kekasi too warned him of the unfortunate outcome of the battle with Rama but Ravana refused to pay any heed.

On the first day of the battle, many
great warriors were massacred.
The following day, Ravana arrived on the
battlefield with his army. Rama confronted

Ravana and a battle raged between the two. Rama destroyed Ravana's chariot. Unarmed and helpless, Ravana returned on foot to his palace. Unnerved by his defeat, Ravana ordered that his younger brother Kumbhakarna be woken up.

Kumbhakarna had performed a yajna to please Lord Brahma. As he wished for a boon from Brahma, his tongue was tied by Goddess Saraswati. Hence, instead of uttering the word "Indraasana" – the seat of Indra – he asked for Nidraasana – the bed for sleeping. And then, Kumbhakarna slipped into deep slumber for months. Now, on Ravana's command, a battalion was sent to awaken Kumbhakarna to add strength to the mighty Lankan army.

RAMAYANA STORIES

The Battle with Kumbhakarna

An imprint of Om Books International

In a cave, the gigantic Kumbhakarna lay asleep. Ravana's battalion sounded hundreds of drums and aimed thousands of weapons at the mighty demon to rouse him from his slumber.

After repeated efforts, Kumbhakarna finally awoke and roared, "Why have you awakened me? I will kill you all." The terrified soldiers said, "Your brother Ravana is in trouble. It is at the master's behest that we came to awaken you."

Sensing urgency, Kumbhakarna went to meet Ravana.

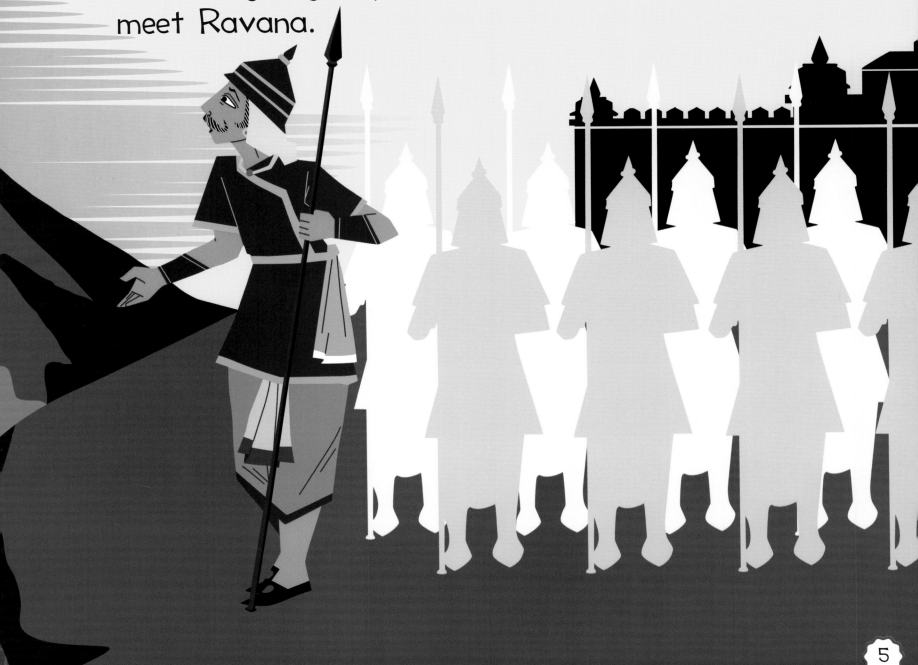

Ravana informed him about the kidnapping of Sita and the battle with Rama. After listening to the complete story, Kumbhakarna replied, "You have made a huge mistake by kidnapping Sita. Rama is not an ordinary mortal. He is an incarnation of Lord Vishnu. We are doomed. Since you are my elder brother, I will fight Rama and even give up my life for you."

Kumbhakarna's entry into the battlefield took Vibhishana by surprise. Greeting his elder brother, Vibhishana recounted how Ravana had insulted him and why he had decided to come to Rama for shelter. He advised Kumbhakarna to follow him.

Kumbhakarna retorted, "Get out of my way, I am not here to take instructions from you. Let me fight Rama." Dismissing Vibhishana, he marched ahead, crushing and killing hundreds of monkeys on his way. Directed by Angada, the monkeys began fighting the enormous Kumbhakarna. Thousands of them clung to him and tried to injure him with their nails and teeth. An agitated Kumbhakarna cast an angry glance at the army of monkeys and killed them.

Even Angada, Sugreeva, Hanuman and Lakshmana failed to overpower Kumbhakarna. Seeing the destruction of his army by the mighty demon, Rama turned to him with his bow and arrow. A fierce battle ensued. Finally, Rama used his Amogh arrows, the ones that never miss their mark, to vanquish Kumbhakarna. As Rama shot the arrows, Kumbhakarna collapsed and died instantly.

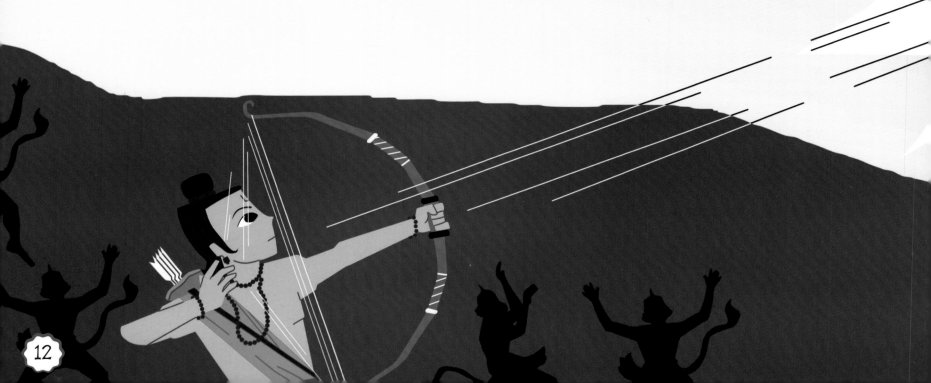

13

Ravana lamented the death of his brave and beloved brother. His sons Atikaya, Narantaka and Devantaka tried to console him, "Rest assured, father. We will destroy

Rama and his entire army. Allow us to go to the battlefield. We will not disappoint you."

Taking stock of the situation, Ravana gave his consent.

Atikaya, Narantaka and Devantaka entered the battlefield with deafening war cries. Atikaya challenged Lakshmana to fight him. A brutal battle followed and in the end, Narantaka and Devantaka were killed.

RAMAYANA STORIES

Lakshmana is Injured

An imprint of Om Books International

After a fierce and long battle, Ravana's son Atikaya was killed. When his mother Dhanyamalini heard of her son's death, she wept bitterly. Ravana was also very sad and

disappointed. Then, Indrajit talked
to Ravana and convinced him that
he would avenge his brother's death
in the battlefield the next day.

The brave Indrajit went into battle. Rama sent Lakshmana to face Indrajit. The monkey army was quite disturbed by Indrajit's arrival. With a deafening roar, he caught both Rama and

Lakshmana in a Nagapasha or noose of serpents. Sugreeva and the others were distraught at this sight.

The gods in heaven protested. They were restless and confused. Filled with pride at such an easy walkover, Indrajit returned to the palace.

Then Hanuman approached Garuda, the vehicle
of Vishnu, and prayed to him to devour the
snakes and free Rama and Lakshmana. As snakes
were Garuda's staple diet, he quickly flew to the
battlefield and freed them from the Nagapasha.
Rama thanked Garuda sincerely.

When Indrajit heard that Rama and Lakshmana
had been freed from the Nagapasha, he flew into

a rage. With huge angry steps, he marched back to the battlefield and challenged Rama and Lakshmana once again.

After seeking Rama's permission, Lakshmana attacked the brave Indrajit and they fought a mighty duel. When Indrajit realised that he alone would not be able to overpower Lakshmana, and was being pushed towards defeat, he used Shakti, the mighty weapon, on Lakshmana.

Immediately, Lakshmana fell down, unconscious. Indrajit tried his best to lift his mighty rival Lakshmana in his arms, but he could not do so. Embarrassed, he left the battlefield. When Hanuman realised that Lakshmana had fainted, he lifted him on his shoulders and took him to Rama. When Rama saw Lakshmana in such a state, he cradled his younger brother in his lap and cried loudly. The army of monkeys was plunged in sorrow and despair.

Vibhishana consoled Rama and told him to fetch Sushena, the physician, from Lanka to treat Lakshmana. In the stealth of the night, Hanuman went to Lanka and brought back Sushena with him. The physician examined Lakshmana and said that there was a herb, the Sanjeevani Booti, that could revive him but it grew only on the peak of a mountain in the Himalayas.

But if Hanuman did not return with the Sanjeevani Booti before sunrise, chances were that Lakshmana would not survive the power of Shakti, the weapon that had felled him.

After seeking Rama's permission,
Hanuman traversed to the Himalayas.
When Ravana learned from his spies
that Hanuman was on his way to fetch the
Sanjeevani Booti from the Himalayas, he
went to the magician Kalnemi and told him

to use his magical powers to halt Hanuman on his way to the Himalayas and kill him through deceit. Kalnemi set about obeying Ravana's orders.

At night, on the Dronagiri Mountain in the Himalayas, all herbs looked alike. Hanuman could not recognise the Sanjeevani Booti, so he lifted the entire Dronagiri Mountain and flew back to Lanka.

As Hanuman flew over Ayodhya, Bharata at Nandigram mistook him for a rakshasa and fired a featherless arrow at him. Hanuman cried out "Shri Rama" and fell to the ground. When Bharata heard him take the name of Rama, he came close to him. He was deeply sad after hearing the entire story of

the battle. He made Hanuman sit on his swiftest arrow and sent him off to Lanka. Hanuman was back before sunrise. With the Sanjeevani Booti, Sushena revived Lakshmana. The army of monkeys was overjoyed to see their beloved Lakshmana healthy again.

When Indrajit received the news of Lakshmana's survival, he decided to pray to Ishtdevi in her cave to seek the boon of invisibility. Vibhishana told Rama that if Indrajit succeeded in conducting this yajna, he would become invincible. Rama sent Angada and the other monkeys to disrupt the yajna, thus, saving the day.

RAMAYANA STORIES

The Death of Ravana

Om KIDZ

An imprint of Om Books International

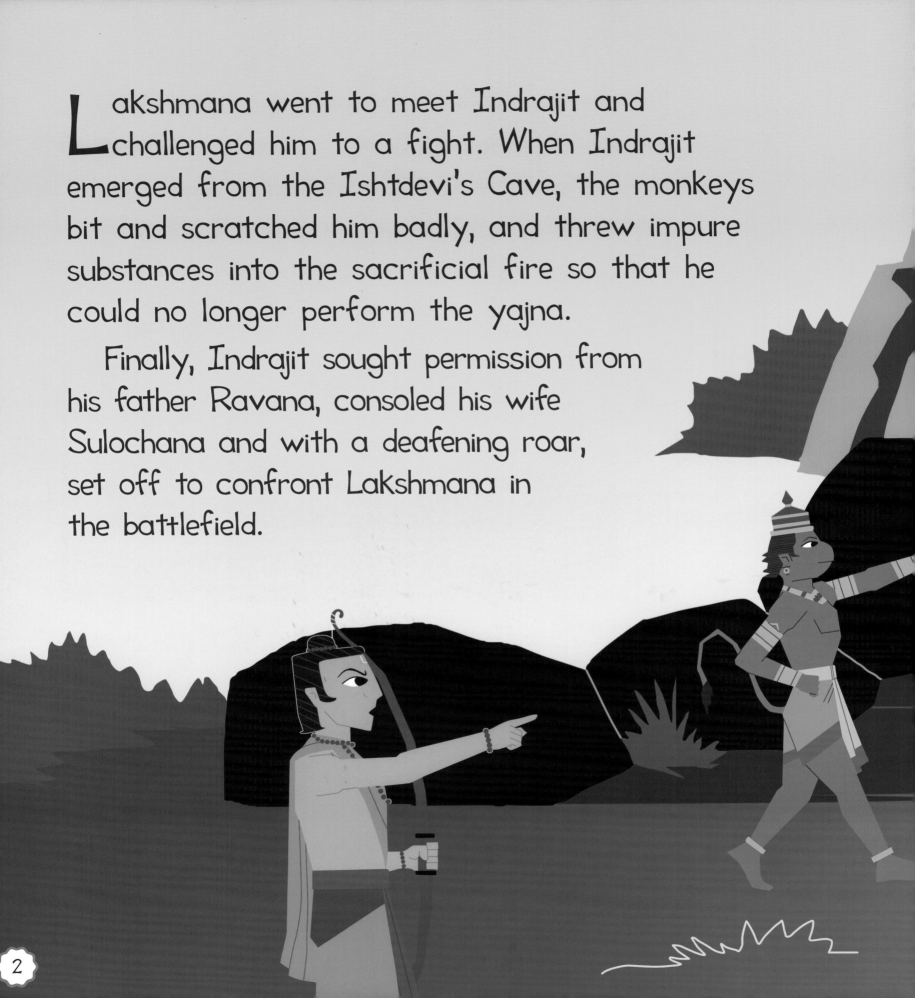

Lakshmana went to meet Indrajit and challenged him to a fight. When Indrajit emerged from the Ishtdevi's Cave, the monkeys bit and scratched him badly, and threw impure substances into the sacrificial fire so that he could no longer perform the yajna.

Finally, Indrajit sought permission from his father Ravana, consoled his wife Sulochana and with a deafening roar, set off to confront Lakshmana in the battlefield.

The two mighty warriors engaged in a fierce battle. Indrajit used many of his magical weapons but

4

Lakshmana was more than a match for him, and countered every move he made deftly. At last, Indrajit was killed by Lakshmana's well-aimed arrow.

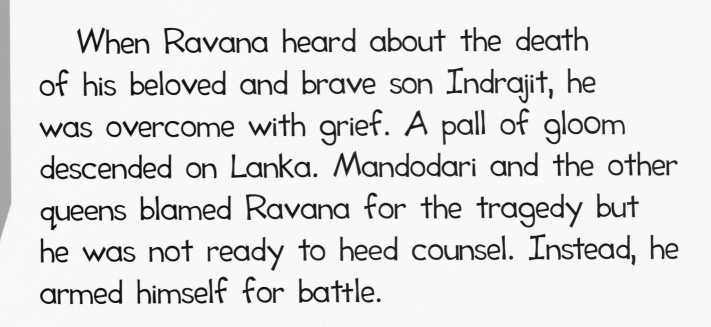

When Ravana heard about the death of his beloved and brave son Indrajit, he was overcome with grief. A pall of gloom descended on Lanka. Mandodari and the other queens blamed Ravana for the tragedy but he was not ready to heed counsel. Instead, he armed himself for battle.

Meanwhile, Rishi Agastya came to Rama and taught him the Aditya Stotra. It was the most powerful prayer in praise of Surya, the Sun God that Rama recited before his battle with Ravana.

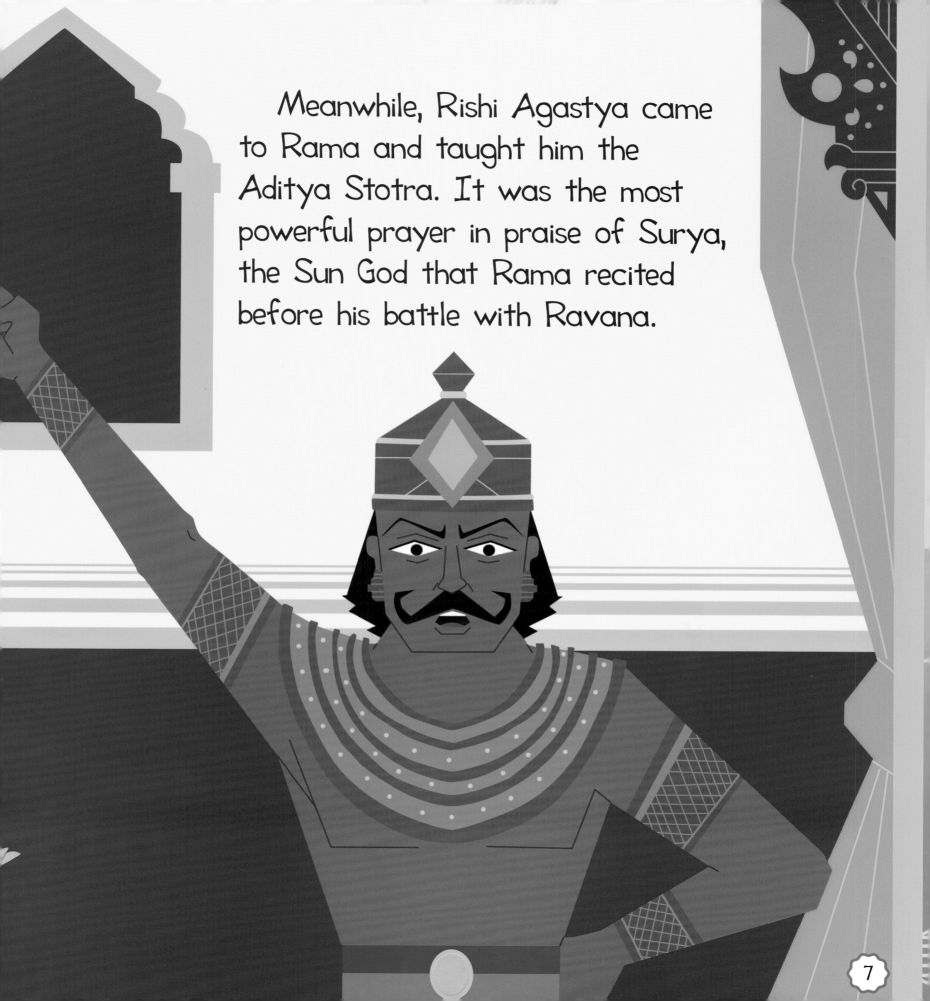

Ravana delivered a rousing speech to his army, urging them to enter the battlefield with renewed enthusiasm. A battle ensued between Rama and Ravana. Injured by Rama's sharp and well-aimed arrows, Ravana fell unconscious in his chariot.
His charioteer quickly

drove him away from the battlefield. But as soon as Ravana regained consciousness, he returned to the battlefield to fight Rama.

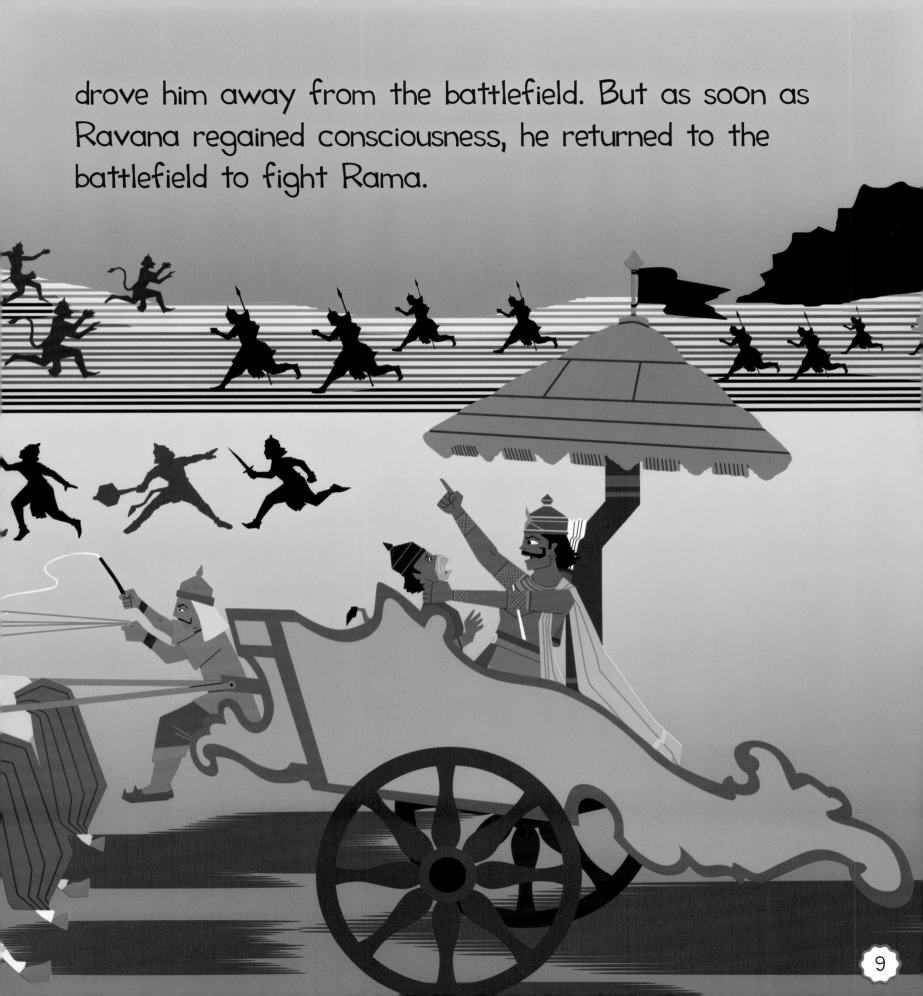

At night, Mandodari requested Ravana to save the clan by going to Rama and seeking his forgiveness. "He is the incarnation of Lord Vishnu. He is

all powerful," she said. Her words fell on deaf ears. Instead, Ravana went to the Mahakal Temple to pray for strength.

When Indra, King of the Devas, saw Rama fighting on foot in the battlefield, he sent his chariot and charioteer and requested Rama to use both in order to kill Ravana. Rama accepted to do so as a mark of respect for the devas.

Ravana used various mysterious and magical devices to distract Rama but Rama rendered all his tricks useless.

In the end, with the
help of the Brahmastra, he
finally killed Ravana, the
demon king of Lanka.

The devas rejoiced. The sound of conch shells and drums announced the celebration of the end of the rakshasas who had terrorised them for so long. They

14

showered flowers on earth. Gandharvas and apsaras, the celestial musicians and dancers, sang and danced to mark the victory.

Meanwhile, Vibhishana mourned the death of his brother and Mandodari wept inconsolably.

Vibhishana performed the last rites of Ravana. Lakshmana, with Rama's blessings, went to the palace of Lanka marking the coronation of Vibhishana as King of Lanka.

RAMAYANA STORIES

Rama Returns
to Ayodhya

An imprint of Om Books International

After fourteen years of vanvas and killing of Ravana, Rama and Sita's return was celebrated as the victory of good over evil. Vibhishana, along with Hanuman and other warriors prepared to welcome Sita to the camp where Rama awaited his wife's return. The army of monkeys was curious to catch a glimpse of Sita.

Before returning to Ayodhya, amidst
the army of monkeys and other warriors,
Sita underwent Agni Pariksha – an ordeal
by fire – after Rama asked her to prove

to prove her purity. What followed was a miracle. Sita emerged from the flames untouched.

To celebrate the death of Ravana, the Demon King, Brahma and Indra, along with all the devas gathered to express their gratitude to Rama and sang praises of his greatness.

Dasharatha, Rama's father, came to bless his son from the heavens above. Rama received the blessings humbly.

Fourteen years of exile were drawing to a close. A worried Rama met Vibhishana, and said, "We have one more day to complete our fourteen years of exile. If I am unable to reach Ayodhya in good time, my brother Bharata will get very anxious. Could you please arrange for the Pushpak Vimana – flying chariot – at once?"

Without further delay, the Vimana was presented before Rama. He asked Vibhishana, Sugreeva, Hanuman, Jambavana, Angada and the entire army of monkeys to board the flying chariot. Then Rama mounted the flying chariot, followed by his brother Lakshmana and wife, Sita.

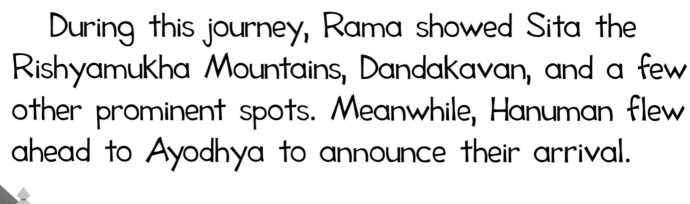

During this journey, Rama showed Sita the Rishyamukha Mountains, Dandakavan, and a few other prominent spots. Meanwhile, Hanuman flew ahead to Ayodhya to announce their arrival.

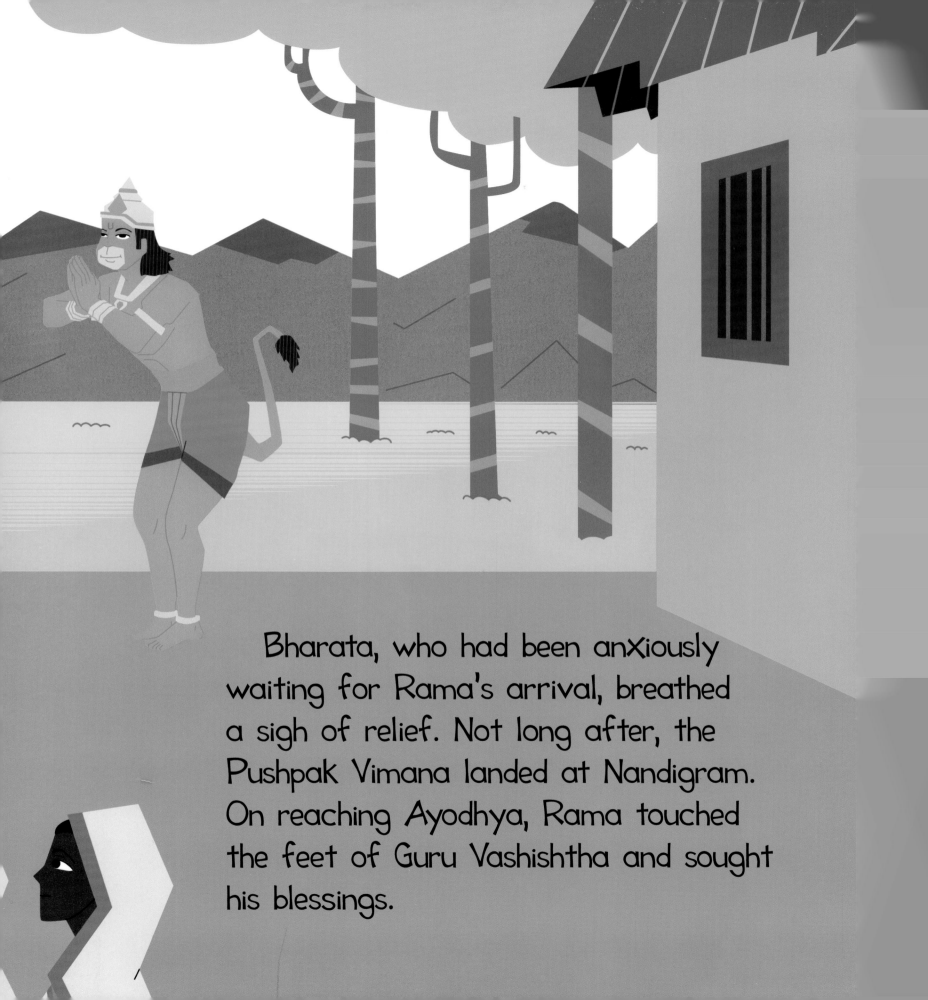

Bharata, who had been anxiously waiting for Rama's arrival, breathed a sigh of relief. Not long after, the Pushpak Vimana landed at Nandigram. On reaching Ayodhya, Rama touched the feet of Guru Vashishtha and sought his blessings.

Rama then greeted his three mothers – Kaushalya, Kaikeyi and Sumitra – with respect and affection.

Turning to Bharata
and Shatrughna,
Rama embraced his
brothers lovingly.

13

With tears of joy in his eyes, Bharata returned the Charanpaduka — wooden clogs — to Rama. This union after fourteen years was memorable. Using his yogic powers, Rama soon assumed diverse forms and split into several parts so that he could greet all the people who had assembled to welcome him. Rama's reunion with his mother, Kaikeyi, was a sight to behold.

Later, the coronation of Rama was celebrated with great pomp and show in Ayodhya. Rama's rule restored peace, prosperity and happiness in his kingdom and the entire universe.

RAMAYANA STORIES

Luv and Kush

Om
KIDZ

An imprint of Om Books International

After Sita's purity was questioned for having lived in Lanka with Ravana, Rama sent her away to live in Sage Valmiki's ashram. Here she assumed the name Vanadevi. During that time, two sons were born to her, named Luv and Kush. Sita kept their birth a secret from Rama. The two boys grew up to be as brave and strong as their father. At an early age, they learnt the scriptures and the use of weapons from Sage Valmiki.

One day, Rama decided to hold an Ashwamedha Yajna. After the rituals were over, according to custom, a sacred white horse was decorated with jewels and expensive garments. This horse would be let loose and it would travel wherever it chose to, with Rama's army following it. A declaration was suspended from the horse's neck which stated that

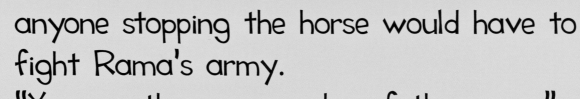

anyone stopping the horse would have to fight Rama's army.

"You are the commander of the army," Rama instructed Shatrughna.

The horse was let loose and the army followed it as it travelled across many lands. One day, as it galloped past Sage Valmiki's ashram, Luv and Kush caught it and took it to the ashram. "Let the horse go!" a furious Shatrughna arrived and ordered the boys.

"You'll have to fight us first,"
Luv replied.

Shatrughna ordered his soldiers to capture the horse. But Luv and Kush defeated his soldiers and him in battle. Shatrughna was forced to flee. He returned and reported everything to Rama.

"These are no ordinary boys. I have never seen archers like them," he said.
"Lakshmana! Go and fetch the horse as well as these boys," Rama ordered.

Lakshmana reached Sage Valmiki's ashram and ordered Luv and Kush to return the horse.

"You'll have to fight us first," Kush replied stubbornly. Both Luv and Kush had learnt the art of warfare from Sage Valmiki and were not scared of Lakshmana's reputation as a warrior.

"I am warning you for the last time. Return the horse now!" Lakshmana intimidated the boys.

"Return this arrow!" Kush said as he shot an arrow at Lakshmana. Soon, a fierce battle began between Lakshmana, Luv and Kush. Lakshmana's anger gave way to genuine admiration at the archery skills

the two boys possessed. But soon, Lakshmana was injured and slumped to the ground. Rama was surprised to hear of Lakshmana's defeat.

"Who are these boys? How can Lakshmana be defeated in battle?" he wondered, "Go to Sage Valmiki's ashram at once," he ordered Bharata. "Take Hanuman and his army of monkeys with you."

When Bharata arrived with his army of monkeys, Luv and Kush valiantly stood their ground. "Look Kush! So many monkeys!" Luv exclaimed. Both started raining arrows on the monkeys who

started fleeing under their assault. Bharata was also forced to surrender after he fell to the ground and Sugreeva was knocked unconscious by the very tree he had uprooted.

"Only the sons of Lord Rama are capable of such feats," Hanuman realised. He lovingly wrapped his tail around Luv and

allowed himself to be captured when Kush came to his brother's rescue. The brothers dragged Hanuman by the tail to Sage Valmiki's ashram.

"Look at the monkey we have captured, mother,"
they announced to Sita.
"O my sons!" Sita exclaimed, "What have you done?
You have captured the great Hanuman."
"I knew it!" Hanuman smiled as he bowed to Sita.

"Go and return the horse at once," Sita instructed Luv and Kush. On their way back, with no intention of returning the horse, they were met by Rama who had arrived with his soldiers after learning of Bharata's defeat. "Who are you?" Rama asked Luv and Kush.

"We are the sons of Vanadevi and the students of Maharishi Valmiki," the boys replied. Rama immediately knew that these two boys were his sons. But Luv and Kush were unaware of this fact and started raining arrows on Rama and his army till Sage Valmiki intervened.

"That is your father, King Rama of Ayodhya," he informed Luv and Kush as Rama hugged his sons and wept tears of joy. Sita watched them from a distance, lovingly. She was happy to have been able to reunite the two worthy princes to their father.

Sita then asked her mother to take her back. Mother Earth split into two and welcomed her into her arms. Sita disappeared into the folds of the earth where she was found by her father, Janaka.